# KUMIHO

The Korean **nine-tailed fox**. A shape-shifting **demoness** that typically takes on the form of a woman before she murders and devours her human prey

I'M HERE FOR YOU, YUN HEE.

BIG SISTER IS HERE FOR YOU.

# The Fox Sister

# CHAPTER 1: Little Sister

Created by **Christina Strain** and **Jayd Aït-Kaci**

SEOUL, SOUTH KOREA
NOVEMBER 22ND, 1968

SEVEN YEARS LATER

SOOT BULL...

sniff sniff

IS IT HERE?

=SNORT=

WE'LL COME BACK AFTER CLASS THEN.

SO--

SOOT BULL!!

‹SOOT, HUH? I'VE ALWAYS WONDERED WHAT HIS NAM--›

‹STAY AWAY FROM MY DOG.›

‹...PLEASE.›

‹ALEX!!›

‹WE ARE WAITING FOR YOU!›

‹SORRY! I'M COMING! I'M COMING!›

14

HANAAAANEEEM DUUOOSHEEP SUEOOOHHH

SHUK SHUK

THAT WAS AMAZING, YUN HEE!

I WANT A CHARM!

A LOVE CHARM!

OH! ME TOO! I WANT A LOVE CHARM MADE BY A REAL PRIESTESS!

WE'LL PAY MORE FOR IT!

YOU'RE FROM KUNSAN, RIGHT?

DO YOU HAVE FAMILY IN SEOUL?

NO.

OH, SO YOUR FAMILY IS ALL BACK IN KU--

THEY'RE ALL DEAD.

ONE THOUSAND WON, PLEASE.

EACH.

CLICK

Love me tender

Love me sweet

Never let me go

You have made my life complete

and I love you so.

<HEY, BOY!>

<HOW ARE Y--〉

SOOT BULL, COME HERE.

<WELL, THAT WAS EMBARRASSING.>

<YES.>

<DO ALL AMERICAN PEOPLE KISS THE DOGS?>

<WHAT? OH NO, I MEANT MY SINGING.>

<ALTHOUGH I HAVE BEEN TOLD THAT I SOUND A LOT LIKE ELVIS.>

‹DO YOU KNOW THIS GIRL?›

‹HER NAME IS CHO SUN HEE.›

‹IS THIS YOU IN THIS PICTURE? YOU WERE REALLY CUTE!›

SWIPE!

‹WAIT WAIT WAIT! I'M SORRY!›

‹I DIDN'T MEAN TO OFFEND YOU.›

‹I DON'T KNOW A CHO SUN HEE.›

‹BUT I CAN SHOW YOU AROUND THE CHURCH, IF YOU'D LIKE.›

24

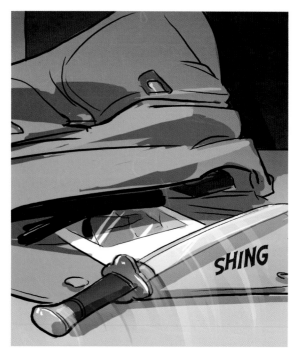

CLICK
POP
SFFFFFFF CLICK

Well, I dated your big sister and took her to a show

I went for some candy along came Jim Dandy

And they snuck right out of the door...

Ev'ry time I see your sister well she's got somebody new

She's mean and she's evil like that old Boll Weevil

Guess I'll try my luck with you

*Little sister, don't you*

*Little sister, don't you*

*Little sister, don't you*

*kiss me once or tw*

‹AYYYYY, SOOT!›

‹I WAS HOPING YOU'D STOP BY.›

‹DO ME A FAVOR...›

‹...AND TAKE THIS TO YOUR OWNER, 'KAY BOY?›

‹READY FOR BREAKFAST, BOY!?›

BARK!

‹I SAVED A TON OF LEFT OVER BULGOGI FOR YOU!›

BARK! BARK BARK!

SOOT BULL, YOU'RE LOOKING FA–

WHAT'S THIS?

34

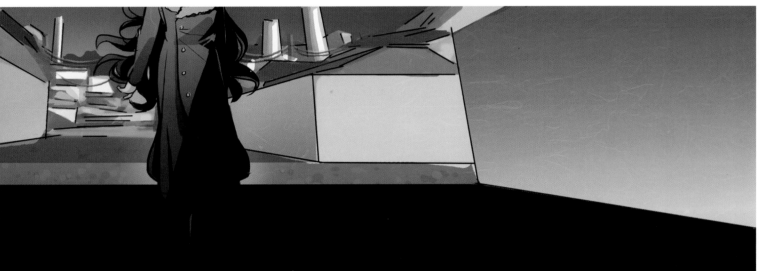

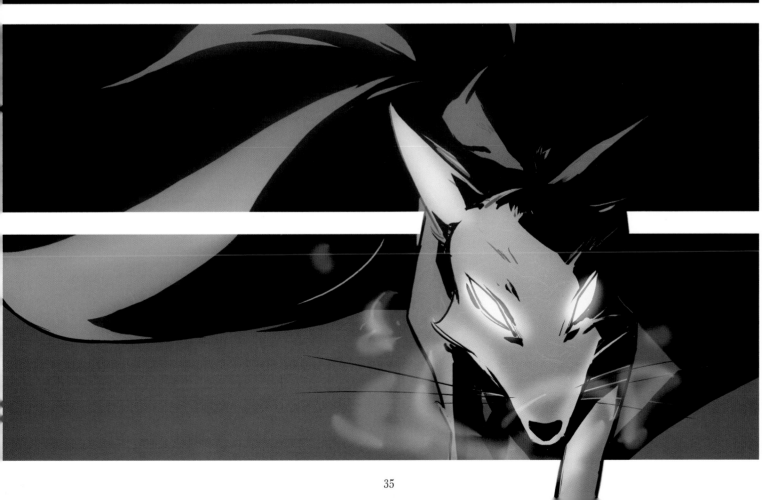

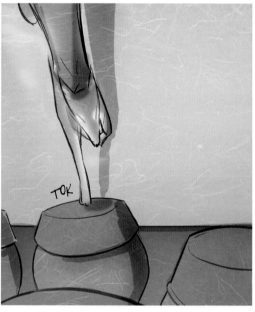

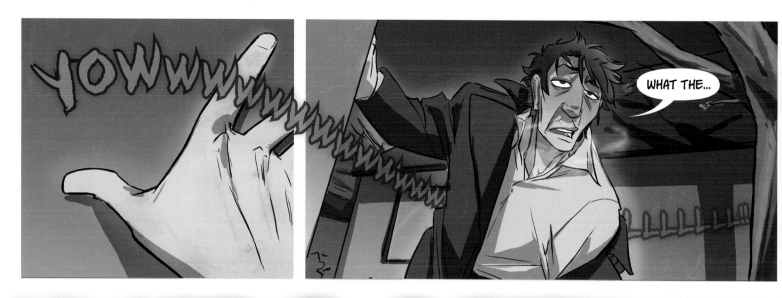

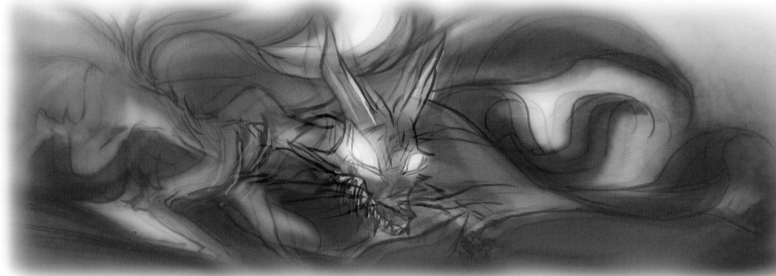

To Be Continued...

# The Fox Sister

Concept Art

Yun Hee

FOXY EYES.

GLORIOUS BROKEN NOSE

I GNORE

ELVIS IMPRESSION

A LITTLE LESS CONVERSATION

Alex

Sun Hee

Kumiho / Soot Bull

CHO
YUN HEE

AGE: 19

HEIGHT: 5'4"

CHO
SUN HEE

AGE: 24

HEIGHT: 5'6"

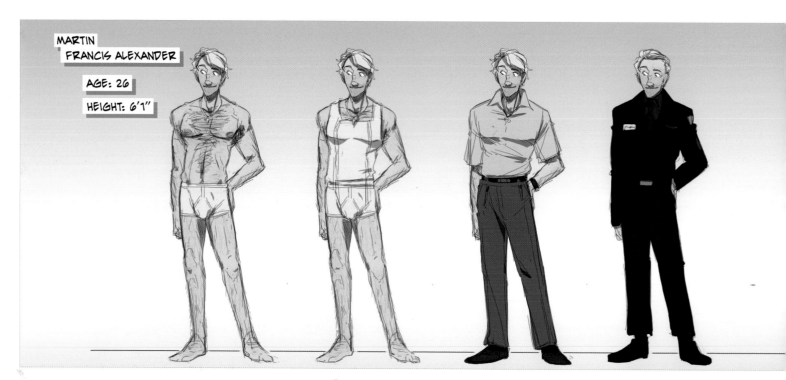

MARTIN
FRANCIS ALEXANDER

AGE: 26

HEIGHT: 6'1"

We'd like to mentally and
typographically thank:

Tu Nguyen, Peter Steigerwald, Fawn Lau,
Han Yee Ling, Nunzio DeFilippis, Emily Warren,
Sarah Magelky, Jen Doyle, and of course
Jon Shiring and Alex Singer.

**Thank you.**
**Thank you.**
**Thank you.**

To read more, go to **thefoxsister.com**

**THE FOX SISTER** Chapter 1

Created by **CHRISTINA STRAIN** and **JAYD AÏT-KACI**
Written by **CHRISTINA STRAIN**
Art by **JAYD AÏT-KACI** with Christina Strain
Design and Production by **FAWN LAU**
Lettering by **DAVE LANPHEAR** and **FAWN LAU**
*The Fox Sister* Logo Designed by **PETER STEIGERWALD**

*Love Me Tender* Lyrics by Elvis Presley © RCA Records and Elvis Presley Music
*Little Sister* Lyrics by Elvis Presley, Doc Pomus and Mort Shuman ©
RCA Records and Elvis Presley Music

First Printing **March 2012**
ISBN: 978-1-4675-1349-4

Printed in CHINA by Global PSD